STRING FIGURES
FROM
AROUND THE WORLD

by
Sorena DeWitt

illustrated by
Robin Michel

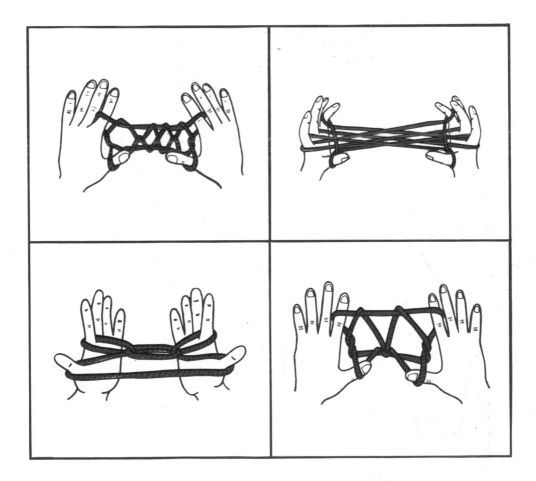

HEIAN

String Figures from Around the World I

Text by Sorena DeWitt
Illustration by Robin Michel

© 1992, Sorena DeWitt
© 1992, Robin Michel

ISBN: 0-89346-356-6

HEIAN INTERNATIONAL, INC.
P.O. BOX 1013
UNION CITY, CA 94587

Printed in Thailand

TABLE OF CONTENTS

STRING FIGURES
FROM AROUND THE WORLD

Introduction

Have you ever made string figures with your hands? This is done by weaving and looping string with your fingers. You can make a picture, tell a story, or even do a trick that looks like magic.

In this age of computer games and fancy toys, there are many childhood games that are in danger of being lost and forgotten. Making string figures is one of these games that is rarely seen anymore.

People all over the world have made string figures a part of their culture. They have used fishing line, leather strips, sinew, or hair that was finely braided. This very old art form has been preserved by anthropologists as they have studied ancient cultures. Sometimes, when the scientists didn't know a language, they would make a string figure to show the people that they were friendly.

Making string figures is fun to do. The more you practice, the easier it becomes. The first string figures shown in this book are the easiest. As you master them, you will want to attempt the more difficult ones. Each string figure has a name, and some tell a story.

Each book in this series contains a sampling of the many string figures found throughout the world. .

INSTRUCTIONS

Making the String

The first step for making string figures is making the string itself. Any kind of string can be used as well as cording or yarn. It needs to be two yards long—one yard long when folded in half and the two ends knotted together to form a circle.

The best knot to use is the square knot which is shown here:

1. Make the first part of the knot by laying the left end of the string over the right end, then tuck the left end under the right string. Pull the ends out far enough to lay the new right string over the left string.

2. Tuck the right string under the left string.

3. Tighten the knot to make as small and as smooth as possible.

String Play Language

In order to follow the directions for each string figure, you need to know the special terms used for parts of your hand, parts of the string, and moves you make with each. The following picture illustrates the hand and string terms:

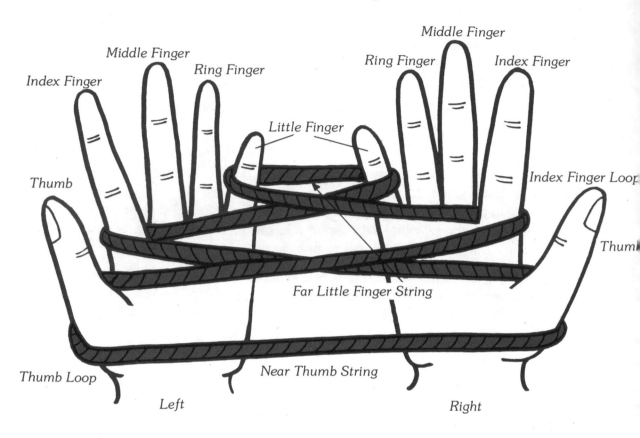

This picture illustrates the string referred to as the *palmar string*:

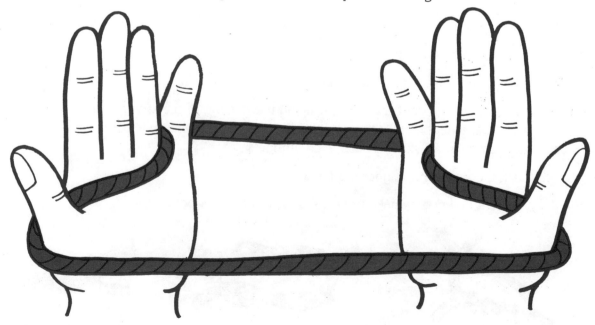

Many of the string figures begin with the same position or opening move. Following are illustrations of those most common in this book's string figures:

Basic Position

Position 1

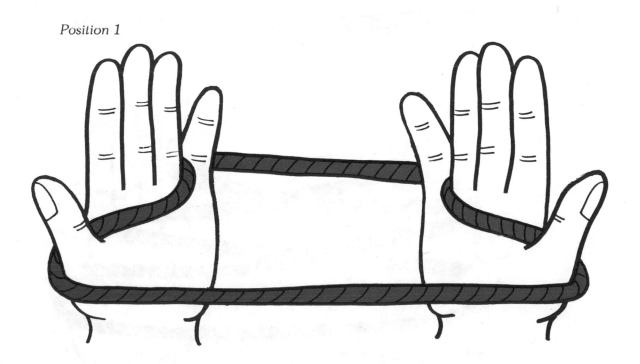

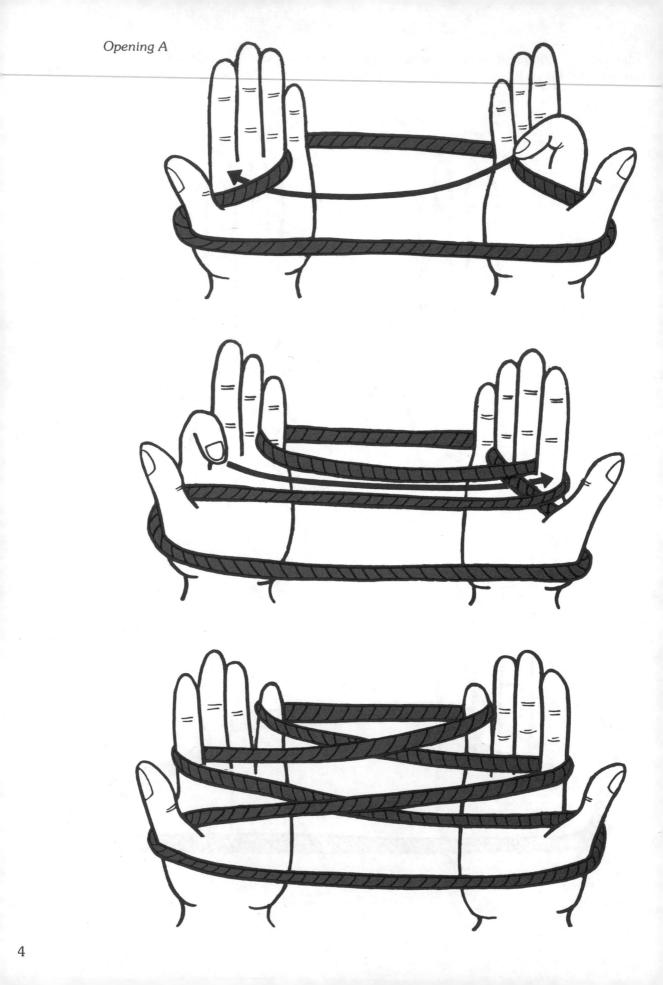

4

Navaho a Loop: This is a common move that you will use often when doing the string figures. It is done by slipping the lower thumb loops over the upper loops and over the thumbs.

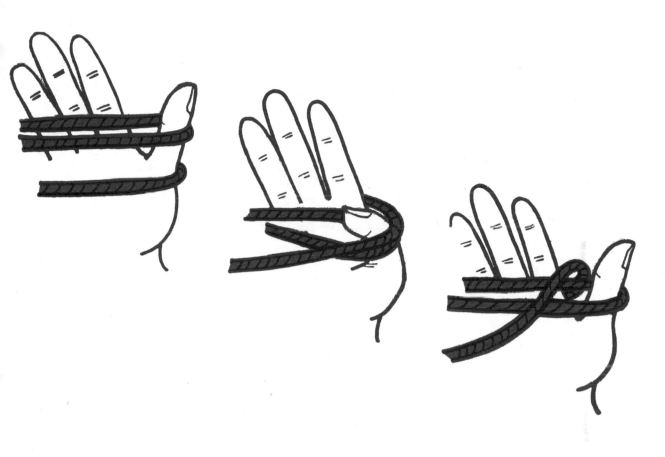

Share a Loop: This is done by pulling out the loop on one finger to also go over a second finger.

Extend: This is done by stretching your fingers out as far as they will go. This is usually done to show the finished figure.

Now that we have covered the basics, let's begin.

Fish Spear

This three-pronged spear was used by people in Alaska and New Guinea; hence its name. It is also known as the Witch's Broom.

1. Begin with Position 1.

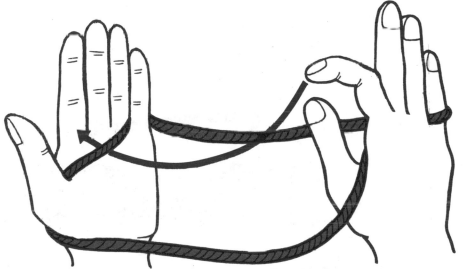

2. Pick up the left palmar string with the right index finger and pull it out half way.

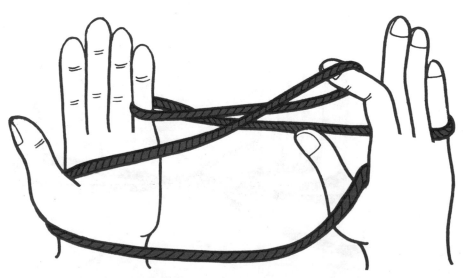

3. Twist this new right index loop by rotating the right index finger away from you, then down, then towards you, and then up. Twist it a second time, being careful not to drop it. Pull this twisted loop as far as possible.

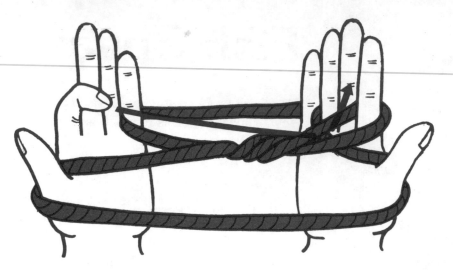

4. Pick up the right palmar string between the right index loop with the left index finger.

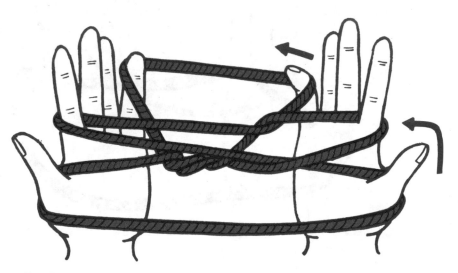

5. Drop your right little finger and right thumb loops.

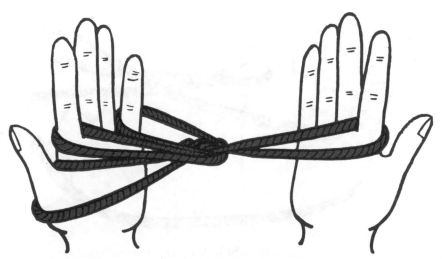

6. Pull with your right index finger and you will see the Fish Spear or Witch's Broom take shape.

Outrigger Canoe

This string figure came from the islands of New Caledonia which are east of Australia. The outrigger canoe was very important to these people. This canoe differs from other canoes because it has a float attached to prevent it from tipping over. For best results, double your string for this figure.

1. Start with Opening A.

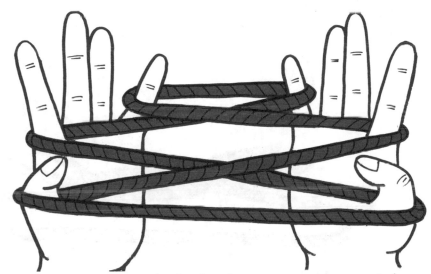

2. With your thumbs, go over the far thumb strings, over the near index strings, and under the far index strings. Pick up these index strings with the back of your thumbs and bring them forward.

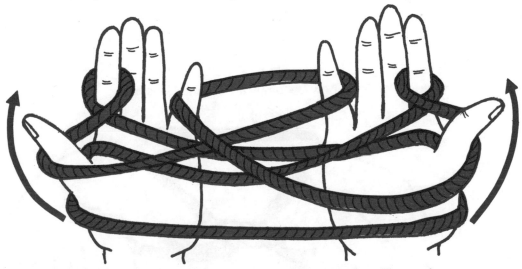

3. This gives you two thumb loops which you now Navaho. This is done by slipping the lower thumb loops over the upper loops and over the thumbs. (See page 5 if you need further instructions.)

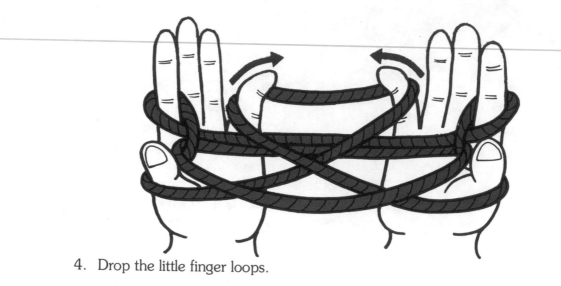

4. Drop the little finger loops.

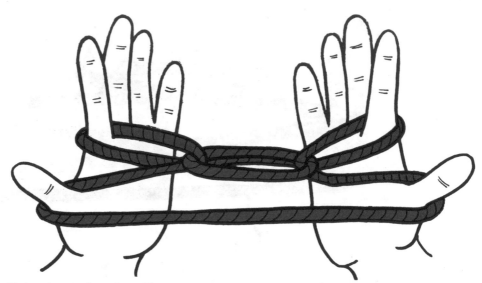

5. Extend your hands to form the Outrigger Canoe.

If you turn your hands so thumbs are up and fingers point down, your Outrigger Canoe now becomes a Cup and Saucer!

The Moth

If you keep the Outrigger Canoe and continue, you end up making a figure that looks like a moth. This is a variation of a string figure that originated with the Zulu tribes of Africa.

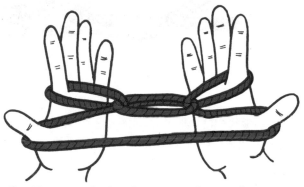

1. Begin with the Outrigger Canoe figure.

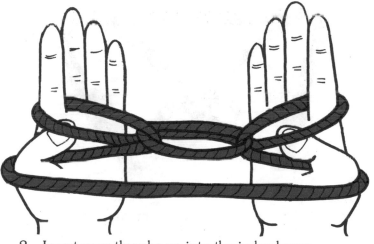

2. Insert your thumbs up into the index loops.

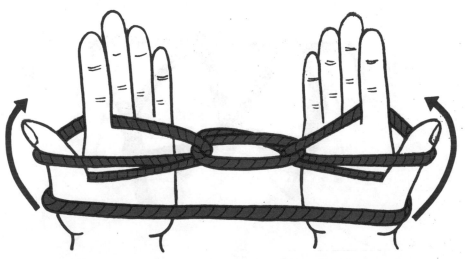

3. Navaho the thumb loops as you did in the Outrigger Canoe.

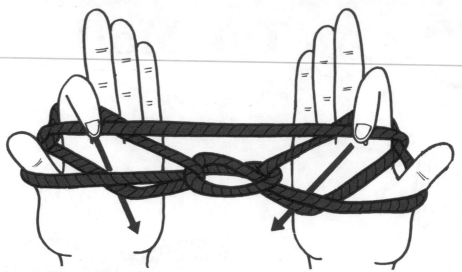

4. Hook your index fingers over the long straight string across the middle and down into the index loops.

5. Holding on tight with your index fingers, turn your hands so the palms face down. The old index loops will slip off.

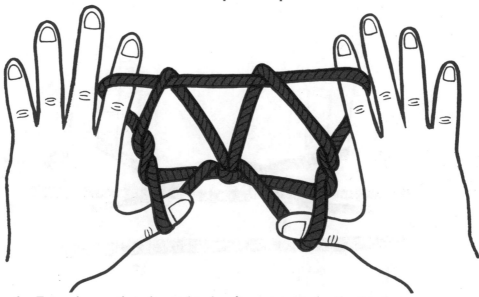

6. Extend your thumbs and index fingers to make the Moth appear.

The Winking Eye

This is a very unique string figure from Hawaii. If you do it just right, you can make it look like the "eye" is really winking.

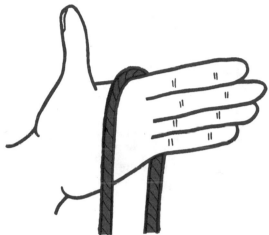

1. Drape the string over your left hand, leaving out the thumb.

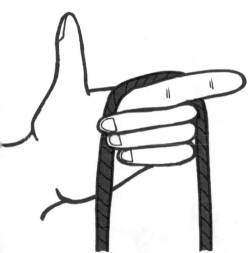

2. Hold onto the string across the palm with your left, middle, ring, and little fingers only.

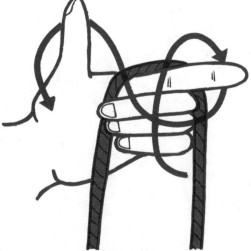

3. Use your right hand to wrap the back string around the left index finger, making a complete loop. Now bring that same string up and in between the index finger and thumb. Bring it behind the left thumb to hang down in front.

4. Pull the new left index finger loop out straight to share it with your left thumb.

5. Take the string of the hanging loop by the thumb and lift it over the thumb so it hangs between the thumb and index finger.

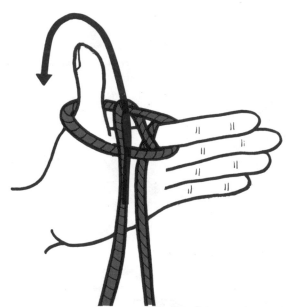

6. Release the three left fingers from the other hanging loop string. Lift this string up and behind the left thumb.

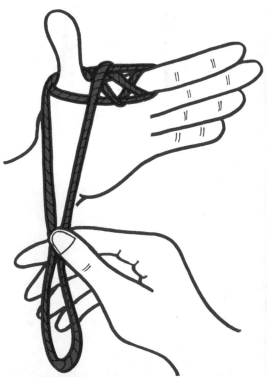

7. This is the eye. To make it wink, pull both strings of the hanging loop. Let go of the strings, extend the thumb and finger, and the eye will open again.

Jacob's Ladder

This is also known as the Fishing Net. It is found in various forms and called by different names throughout the world. The American Indians call it Jacob's Ladder.

1. Do Opening A.

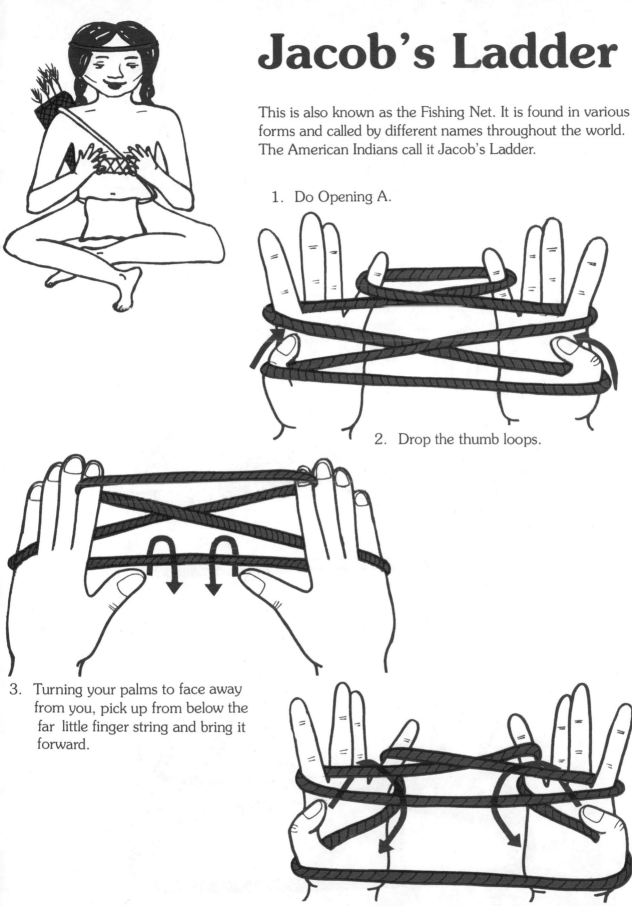

2. Drop the thumb loops.

3. Turning your palms to face away from you, pick up from below the far little finger string and bring it forward.

4. Your thumbs go over the near index strings and under the far index strings to bring it forward.

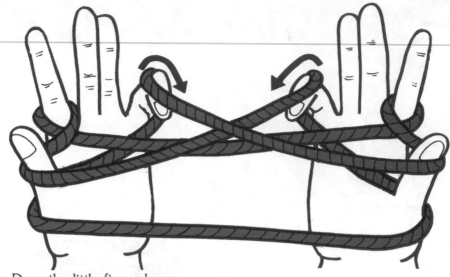

5. Drop the little finger loops.

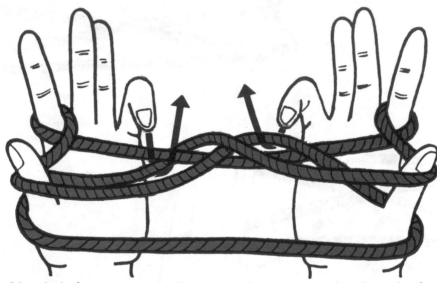

6. Your little fingers go over the near index strings and pick up the far thumb strings.

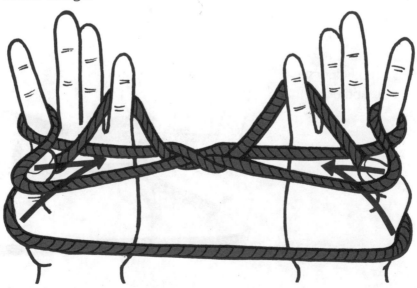

7. Drop the thumb loops.

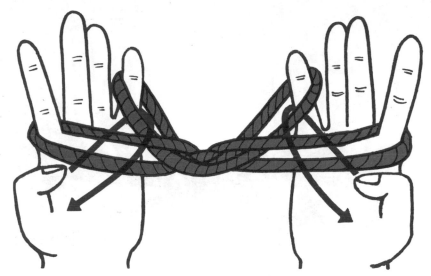

8. Your thumbs go over both index strings and get the near little finger strings and bring them forward.

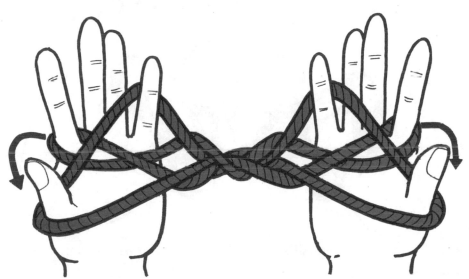

9. With your right hand, pull out the left index loop and share it with the left thumb. Do the same with the right index loop onto the right thumb.

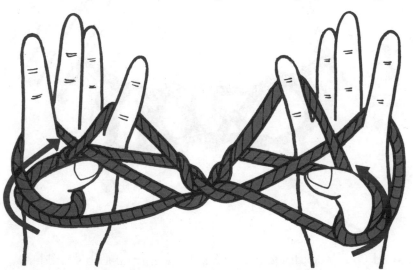

10. Navaho the loops on both thumbs.

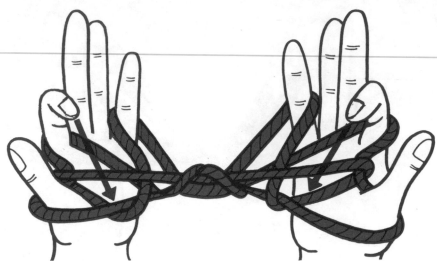

11. Put both index fingers down into the triangles formed between the index fingers and the thumbs.

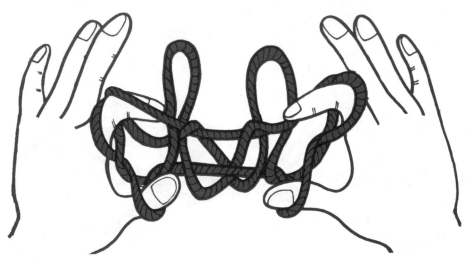

12. Carefully drop your little finger loops and turn your hands so the palms face away from you.

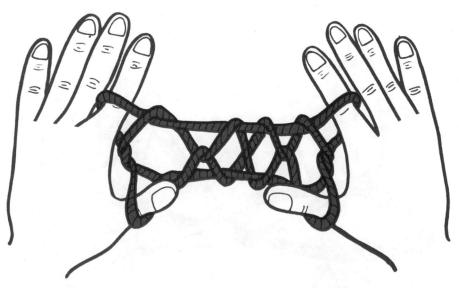

13. Extend your index fingers and thumbs to form Jacob's Ladder.

Japanese Koto

This is a musical instrument that plays a major part in the musical culture of Japan. It is like a harp that lies on the floor.

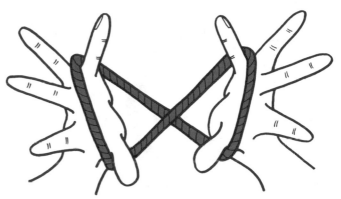

1. Begin with Position 1, except have the strings cross in the middle.

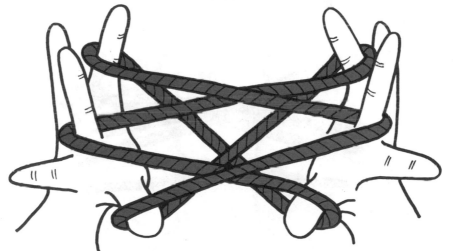

2. Do Opening A using the middle fingers.

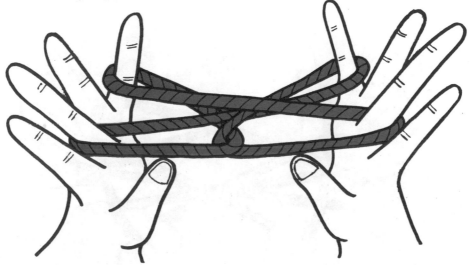

3. Drop the thumb loops.

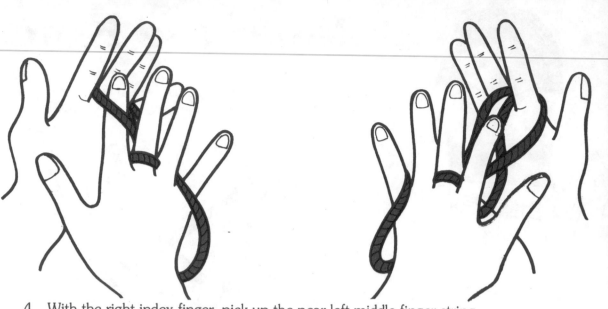

4. With the right index finger, pick up the near left middle finger string. Before pulling your hands apart all the way, use your left index finger to pick up the near right middle finger string going through the newly created right index finger loop.

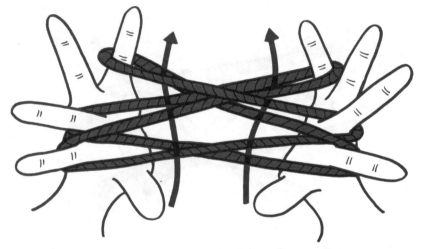

5. Going over the center, pick up the near little finger strings with the thumbs …

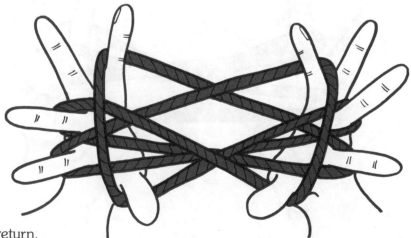

and return.

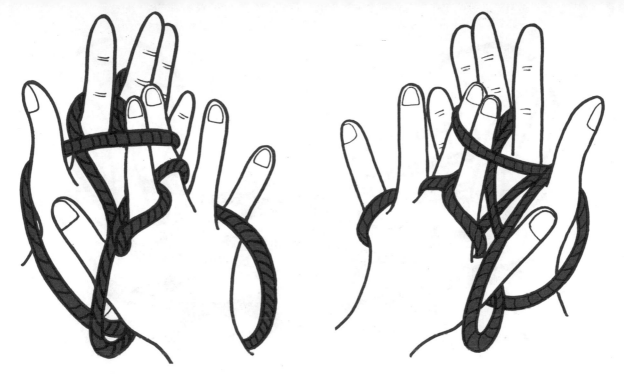

6. Do Opening A using both index and middle fingers.

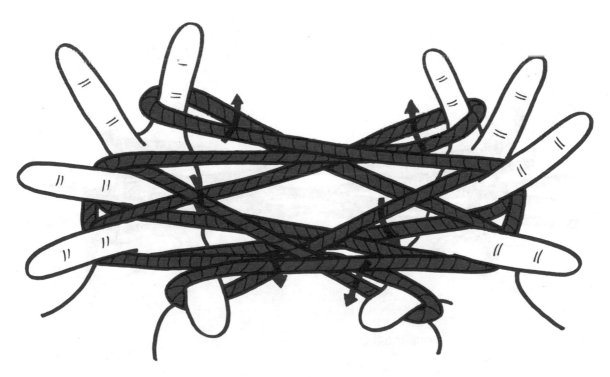

7. Using the right index finger and thumb, untwist the loops on the little finger, middle finger, and thumb of the left hand. When untwisting the middle finger loop, be careful not to disturb the loop around both the middle finger and the index finger. Using the left index finger and thumb, do the same to the right little finger, middle finger, and thumb loops.

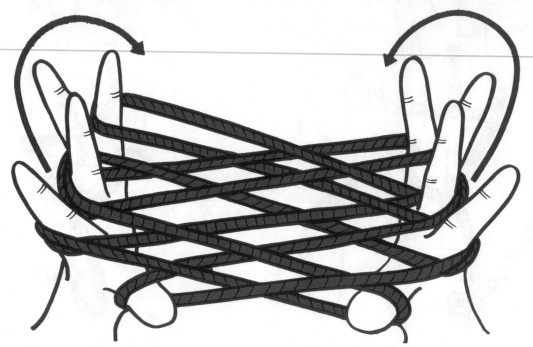

8. Using the index fingers and thumbs again, bring the loop behind both the middle finger and the index finger up over those two fingers into the center of the figure. Do this to each hand.

9. Pull apart to make the Japanese Koto.

Yam Thief

This string figure is both a story and a trick. Yams are very common in South America, where this story is told.

1. Drape the string over your left hand with your thumb on top.

2. With your right index finger, go in under the front string, then in between the left thumb and index finger, and pick up the back string.

Story:

Once there was a yam farmer who saw it was time to harvest his yam crop. (The thumb is the farmer, the fingers are the yams.)

Pull it forward under the front string to make a short loop.

3. Twist this loop once clockwise to make an X. Being careful not to twist this loop again, put it on the left index finger.

4. Tighten the hanging strings. Doing this step correctly is very important. This is your first bag of yams.

5. Repeat steps 2 and 3 for the middle finger on the left hand using the right index finger to go under the front hanging string and in between the left index finger and middle finger to pick up the back string. This new loop to put around the middle finger will make the second bag of yams.

Story:

He got up early the next morning and harvested a whole bag of yams.

The farmer saw many more yams ready for harvest and decided to gather another bag.

Story:

The farmer was very tired, but decided to gather one more bag of yams.

6. Repeat steps 2 and 3 to make a loop on your left ring finger, except pick up the loop between the middle and ring fingers. This will be the third bag of yams.

The farmer looked out over his field and saw that he could finish the harvest by gathering one more bag.

7. Repeat steps 2 and 3 to make a loop on your left little finger, getting the loop from the back string between the ring and little fingers. This will be the fourth bag of yams. Tighten the hanging strings.

The farmer was very, very tired after harvesting all day long. He decided to go to bed early so he could take his yams to market the next morning.

8. Lay your left thumb down against your left fingers to show the farmer lying down in bed.

In the middle of the night, the farmer heard a noise that woke him up.

9. Lift up your left thumb again.

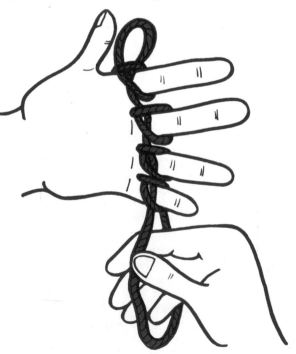

Story:

He was afraid someone was trying to steal his yams. He quickly got out of bed and went to check his harvest.

10. Take the thumb out of its loop.

He checked in front of the bags. He checked in back of the bags.

11. Use your left thumb to go up and down in front of the left fingers and to peek over the back of your left hand.

While the farmer was checking in back of the bags of yams, the thief grabbed them and was gone in an instant.

12. Pull the front string of the hanging loop. Where did they go?

Hint: If this trick doesn't work, the loops weren't twisted correctly on each finger.

RESOURCE LIST

Ayatori Itotori 1, 2, 3, Tama Saito, Fukuinkan, Tokyo.

Cat's Cradle, Owl's Eyes: A Book of String Games, Camilla Gryski, William· Morrow and Company, New York.

Fun with String Figures, W. W. Rouse Ball, Dover Publications, New York.

Story Vine, Anne Pellowski, Macmillan Publishing Co. Inc., New York.

String Figures and How To Make Them, Caroline Furness Jayne, Dover Publications, Inc., New York.

About the Author:

SORENA DeWITT lives in Fremont, California, with her husband and five children. She has taught cultural refinement classes, served on many educational committees, and co-authored the children's almanac, *Guess What Day It Is*.

About the Illustrator:

ROBIN MICHEL has taught arts and crafts for children and is actively involved with art programs in various schools. She lives in Fremont, California, with her husband and three children.